Use Your
Girl
Power
A Journal

Ashley Rice

Blue Mountain Press™
Boulder, Colorado

This journal
belongs to a girl
who has girl power: you!

(your name here)

ISBN: 978-1-68088-077-9

ꟑ and Blue Mountain Press are registered in U.S. Patent and Trademark Office.
Certain trademarks are used under license.

Printed in China.
Second Printing: 2017

Blue Mountain Arts, Inc.
P.O. Box 4549, Boulder, Colorado 80306

This journal is all about using your girl power!
What does girl power mean to you?

_____

_____

_____

_____

_____

_____

_____

_____

_____

_____

_____

_____

_____

_____

_____

_____

_____

_____

HELLO WORLD!

How will you use girl power to change the world?

There are girls who use their girl power
to change the world every day...
girls like you.

You are meant for great things.

What makes you unique?

_____

_____

_____

_____

_____

_____

_____

_____

_____

_____

_____

_____

_____

_____

_____

_____

_____

_____

_____

_____

_____

_____

_____

_____

_____

_____

_____

_____

_____

_____

_____

_____

_____

_____

_____

Don't be afraid to be a little different.
Your uniqueness is one of the most
incredible things about you.

Believe in what you do
and who you are... and you'll go far.

If you were going to make
a soundtrack of your life,
which songs and lyrics would be in it?

_____

_____

_____

_____

_____

_____

_____

_____

_____

_____

_____

_____

_____

_____

_____

_____

_____

_____

Some days you just gotta
forget it all... and dance!

If anyone tries to tell you that you can't sing your own song or make your way in the world... prove them wrong.

Whom is it easiest to be yourself around?
Whom is it difficult to be yourself around?
Why do you think that is?

_____

_____

_____

_____

_____

_____

_____

_____

_____

_____

_____

_____

_____

_____

_____

_____

_____

_____

_____

_____

_____

_____

_____

_____

_____

_____

_____

_____

_____

_____

_____

_____

_____

_____

_____

_____

Don't worry about what
others think. Just be
yourself, and the rest will
take care of itself.

If you are your best self,
you will shine brightly and lead the way
for others to be their best selves.

_____

_____

_____

_____

_____

_____

_____

_____

_____

_____

_____

_____

_____

_____

_____

_____

_____

_____

Whom do you love, and why?

_____

_____

_____

_____

_____

_____

_____

_____

_____

_____

_____

_____

_____

_____

_____

_____

_____

You can love your family, your pets,
and your friends. Love never ends.

Love will bring out the very best in you.

Family is one of the most important things in life. If you've got your family, you've got someone to make every day a little bit brighter and your smile a lot wider. Write down some of your favorite family memories.

_____

_____

_____

_____

_____

_____

_____

_____

_____

_____

_____

_____

_____

_____

_____

_____

_____

You belong to a long line of women
who began as girls dreaming —
and grew up to make a difference.

What does it mean to you to be a good friend?

_____

_____

_____

_____

_____

_____

_____

_____

_____

_____

_____

_____

_____

_____

_____

_____

Who are your closest friends, and why?

_____

_____

_____

_____

_____

_____

_____

_____

_____

_____

_____

_____

_____

_____

_____

_____

_____

_____

Make friends with yourself, and be the best
friend you can be to others.

In the end, friends are what matter most.

Write about some of the women you look up to — either celebrities or people in your life. What qualities do they have that you'd like to see more of in yourself?

_____

_____

_____

_____

_____

_____

_____

_____

_____

_____

_____

_____

_____

_____

_____

_____

_____

_____

_____

_____

_____

_____

_____

_____

_____

_____

_____

_____

_____

_____

_____

_____

_____

_____

_____

_____

_____

_____

_____

_____

_____

You are an amazing girl with grace and talent. What you do now will influence generations of girls to come.

What do you want your career to be someday?

_____

_____

_____

_____

_____

_____

_____

_____

_____

_____

_____

_____

_____

_____

_____

_____

_____

You can write a book. You can start a band.
You can become a doctor. You can dream and plan.

You can do most anything
you put your mind to.

A dream is a song that begins in your heart. It comes from your own imagination. It gives you courage. It makes you strong.

What is your greatest dream?

How do you plan to make that dream a reality?

_____

_____

_____

_____

_____

_____

_____

_____

_____

_____

_____

_____

_____

_____

_____

_____

_____

_____

_____

A dream gives you a place from which to start making your life the way you want it to be.

_____

_____

_____

_____

_____

_____

_____

_____

_____

_____

_____

_____

_____

_____

_____

_____

_____

_____

_____

_____

_____

What challenges are you facing right now?

_____

_____

_____

_____

_____

_____

_____

_____

_____

_____

_____

_____

_____

_____

_____

_____

_____

_____

_____

_____

_____

_____

_____

_____

_____

_____

What are some big or small steps you could take to overcome these challenges?

_____

_____

_____

_____

_____

_____

_____

_____

_____

_____

_____

_____

_____

_____

_____

_____

_____

_____

_____

_____

Never surrender — even when something
stands in your way. There are stars
to find and mountains to climb, and
you'll get there one day.

What is the most courageous thing you've ever done, and what happened because of it?

_____

_____

_____

_____

_____

_____

_____

_____

_____

_____

_____

_____

_____

_____

_____

_____

_____

_____

What would you do if you had
all the courage in the world?

_____

_____

_____

_____

_____

_____

_____

_____

_____

_____

_____

_____

_____

_____

_____

_____

 You are brave and true
and courageous and strong.

You deserve the best in life.
So show your true colors.
Step out into the light and shine!

Write down some things
you're stressed or worried about...
then let them go.

That tangled mess that's got you worried —
it's just a dark cloud...

...and there's a Rainbow
on the other side.

_____

_____

_____

_____

_____

_____

_____

_____

_____

_____

_____

_____

_____

_____

_____

_____

_____

_____

_____

_____

You can handle adversity.
You can stand up tall.

Name some of the things
you like to do that are just for you
and why you enjoy them.

_____

_____

_____

_____

_____

_____

_____

_____

_____

_____

_____

_____

_____

_____

_____

_____

You deserve a
much-needed break!

Make time each day to slow down, kick up
your feet, and let the moment overtake you.

It's okay to make mistakes — they're part of what helps you learn, and they make you who you are. Write about a time when you made a mistake and what you learned from it.

_____

_____

_____

_____

_____

_____

_____

_____

_____

_____

_____

_____

_____

_____

_____

_____

Stay positive in all things,
and always look on the bright side.

What is
your biggest
accomplishment in life,
and what does
it mean
to you?

_____

_____

_____

_____

_____

_____

_____

_____

_____

_____

_____

_____

_____

_____

_____

_____

_____

_____

_____

_____

Sometimes no one is going to tell you that
you are doing a good job except yourself.
So tell yourself that!

Feeling blue? You can write down
all your sad feelings here.

_____

_____

_____

_____

_____

_____

_____

_____

_____

_____

_____

_____

_____

_____

_____

_____

_____

_____

_____

_____

_____

_____

_____

_____

_____

_____

_____

_____

_____

_____

_____

_____

_____

_____

_____

_____

_____

_____

Everybody gets sad sometimes.
And crying and hurting — like
laughing and dreaming — are just
things that people do.

When things are difficult, Reflect on where you are and where you want to go.

Write down the things
that make you happy.

_____

_____

_____

_____

_____

_____

_____

_____

_____

_____

_____

_____

_____

_____

_____

_____

_____

_____

_____

_____

_____

Hold the things that make you
happy close in your heart...
They'll keep you strong.

Your happiness is in your own hands,
and it's up to you to make your life
turn out as great as you know it can be.

Fill these pages with all the things you like about yourself and that make you great.

_____

_____

_____

_____

_____

_____

_____

_____

_____

_____

_____

_____

_____

_____

_____

_____

_____

_____

_____

_____

_____

_____

_____

_____

_____

_____

_____

_____

_____

_____

_____

_____

_____

_____

_____

_____

You are someone with a very special heart and a very special way of being yourself.

Listen to your heart. What is it telling you?

_____

_____

_____

_____

_____

_____

_____

_____

_____

_____

_____

_____

_____

_____

_____

_____

_____

_____

_____

_____

_____

When your mind does not know what to say... your heart will find a way.

_____

_____

_____

_____

_____

_____

_____

_____

_____

_____

_____

_____

_____

_____

_____

_____

_____

_____

_____

You are your own best adviser,
your own best dream maker,
mapmaker, and compass.

What are your hopes for the future — for your own life and for the world?

_____

_____

_____

_____

_____

_____

_____

_____

_____

_____

_____

_____

_____

_____

_____

_____

_____

_____

_____

_____

_____

One day, you will move mountains and
write your name across the sky.

You've got so much to look forward to,
and so many exciting adventures
lie before you.

Write a letter to your future self containing everything you most want to Remember or know later in life.

Remember: with girl power in your heart, you can change the world!

You are a very
special star...

_____

_____

_____

_____

_____

_____

_____

_____

_____

_____

_____

_____

_____

_____

Go on and shine.